CLIFF

PERSONAL INFORMATION

NAME:

ADDRESS:

PHONE:

E-MAIL:

IN AN EMERGENCY PLEASE CONTACT

NAME:

ADDRESS:

PHONE:

DOCTOR PHONE:

KNOWN ALLERGIES:

2022

JANUARY

M	T	W	T	F	S	S
					1	2
3	4	5	6	7	8	9
10	11	12	13	14	15	16
17	18	19	20	21	22	23
24	25	26	27	28	29	30
31						

FEBRUARY

M	T	W	T	F	S	S
	1	2	3	4	5	6
7	8	9	10	11	12	13
14	15	16	17	18	19	20
21	22	23	24	25	26	27
28						

MARCH

M	T	W	T	F	S	S
	1	2	3	4	5	6
7	8	9	10	11	12	13
14	15	16	17	18	19	20
21	22	23	24	25	26	27
28	29	30	31			

APRIL

M	T	W	T	F	S	S
				1	2	3
4	5	6	7	8	9	10
11	12	13	14	15	16	17
18	19	20	21	22	23	24
25	26	27	28	29	30	

MAY

M	T	W	T	F	S	S
						1
2	3	4	5	6	7	8
9	10	11	12	13	14	15
16	17	18	19	20	21	22
23	24	25	26	27	28	29
30	31					

JUNE

M	T	W	T	F	S	S
		1	2	3	4	5
6	7	8	9	10	11	12
13	14	15	16	17	18	19
20	21	22	23	24	25	26
27	28	29	30			

JULY

M	T	W	T	F	S	S
				1	2	3
4	5	6	7	8	9	10
11	12	13	14	15	16	17
18	19	20	21	22	23	24
25	26	27	28	29	30	31

AUGUST

M	T	W	T	F	S	S
1	2	3	4	5	6	7
8	9	10	11	12	13	14
15	16	17	18	19	20	21
22	23	24	25	26	27	28
29	30	31				

SEPTEMBER

M	T	W	T	F	S	S
			1	2	3	4
5	6	7	8	9	10	11
12	13	14	15	16	17	18
19	20	21	22	23	24	25
26	27	28	29	30		

OCTOBER

M	T	W	T	F	S	S
					1	2
3	4	5	6	7	8	9
10	11	12	13	14	15	16
17	18	19	20	21	22	23
24	25	26	27	28	29	30
31						

NOVEMBER

M	T	W	T	F	S	S
	1	2	3	4	5	6
7	8	9	10	11	12	13
14	15	16	17	18	19	20
21	22	23	24	25	26	27
28	29	30				

DECEMBER

M	T	W	T	F	S	S
			1	2	3	4
5	6	7	8	9	10	11
12	13	14	15	16	17	18
19	20	21	22	23	24	25
26	27	28	29	30	31	

2023

JANUARY

M	T	W	T	F	S	S
						1
2	3	4	5	6	7	8
9	10	11	12	13	14	15
16	17	18	19	20	21	22
23	24	25	26	27	28	29
30	31					

FEBRUARY

M	T	W	T	F	S	S
		1	2	3	4	5
6	7	8	9	10	11	12
13	14	15	16	17	18	19
20	21	22	23	24	25	26
27	28					

MARCH

M	T	W	T	F	S	S
		1	2	3	4	5
6	7	8	9	10	11	12
13	14	15	16	17	18	19
20	21	22	23	24	25	26
27	28	29	30	31		

APRIL

M	T	W	T	F	S	S
					1	2
3	4	5	6	7	8	9
10	11	12	13	14	15	16
17	18	19	20	21	22	23
24	25	26	27	28	29	30

MAY

M	T	W	T	F	S	S
1	2	3	4	5	6	7
8	9	10	11	12	13	14
15	16	17	18	19	20	21
22	23	24	25	26	27	28
29	30	31				

JUNE

M	T	W	T	F	S	S
			1	2	3	4
5	6	7	8	9	10	11
12	13	14	15	16	17	18
19	20	21	22	23	24	25
26	27	28	29	30		

JULY

M	T	W	T	F	S	S
					1	2
3	4	5	6	7	8	9
10	11	12	13	14	15	16
17	18	19	20	21	22	23
24	25	26	27	28	29	30
31						

AUGUST

M	T	W	T	F	S	S
	1	2	3	4	5	6
7	8	9	10	11	12	13
14	15	16	17	18	19	20
21	22	23	24	25	26	27
28	29	30	31			

SEPTEMBER

M	T	W	T	F	S	S
				1	2	3
4	5	6	7	8	9	10
11	12	13	14	15	16	17
18	19	20	21	22	23	24
25	26	27	28	29	30	

OCTOBER

M	T	W	T	F	S	S
						1
2	3	4	5	6	7	8
9	10	11	12	13	14	15
16	17	18	19	20	21	22
23	24	25	26	27	28	29
30	31					

NOVEMBER

M	T	W	T	F	S	S
		1	2	3	4	5
6	7	8	9	10	11	12
13	14	15	16	17	18	19
20	21	22	23	24	25	26
27	28	29	30			

DECEMBER

M	T	W	T	F	S	S
				1	2	3
4	5	6	7	8	9	10
11	12	13	14	15	16	17
18	19	20	21	22	23	24
25	26	27	28	29	30	31

CLIFF

2023 NOTABLE DATES

JANUARY

1 NEW YEAR'S DAY

2 NEW YEAR HOLIDAY

3 BANK HOLIDAY (SCOTLAND)

22 CHINESE NEW YEAR (RABBIT)

FEBRUARY

14 VALENTINE'S DAY

21 SHROVE TUESDAY

MARCH

1 ST. DAVID'S DAY

17 ST. PATRICK'S DAY

19 MOTHERING SUNDAY (UK)

22 RAMADAN BEGINS

26 DAYLIGHT SAVING TIME STARTS

APRIL

5 PASSOVER BEGINS

7 GOOD FRIDAY

9 EASTER SUNDAY

10 EASTER MONDAY

22 EARTH DAY

23 ST. GEORGE'S DAY

MAY

1 EARLY MAY BANK HOLIDAY

29 SPRING BANK HOLIDAY

JUNE

18 FATHER'S DAY (UK)

JULY

12 PUBLIC HOLIDAY (NORTHERN IRELAND)

18 ISLAMIC NEW YEAR BEGINS

AUGUST

7 SUMMER BANK HOLIDAY (SCOTLAND)

28 SUMMER BANK HOLIDAY (ENG, NIR, WAL)

SEPTEMBER

15 ROSH HASHANAH (JEWISH NEW YEAR) BEGINS

21 INTERNATIONAL DAY OF PEACE (UNITED NATIONS)

24 YOM KIPPUR BEGINS

OCTOBER

10 WORLD MENTAL HEALTH DAY

29 DAYLIGHT SAVING TIME ENDS

31 HALLOWEEN

NOVEMBER

5 GUY FAWKES NIGHT

12 DIWALI / REMEMBRANCE SUNDAY

30 ST. ANDREW'S DAY

DECEMBER

25 CHRISTMAS DAY

26 BOXING DAY

31 NEW YEAR'S EVE

Photograph by Sue Andrews

PLANNER

JANUARY		FEBRUARY	
1		1 W	
2 M		2 T	
3 T		3 F	
4 W		4 S	
5 T		5 S	
6 F		6 M	
7 S		7 T	
8 S		8 W	
9 M		9 T	
10 T		10 F	
11 W		11 S	
12 T		12 S	
13 F		13 M	
14 S		14 T	
15 S		15 W	
16 M		16 T	
17 T		17 F	
18 W		18 S	
19 T		19 S	
20 F		20 M	
21 S		21 T	
22 S		22 W	
23 M		23 T	
24 T		24 F	
25 W		25 S	
26 T		26 S	
27 F		27 M	
		28 T	
30 M			
31 T			

MARCH	APRIL
1 W	1 S
2 T	2 S
3 F	3 M
4 S	4 T
5 S	5 W
6 M	6 T
7 T	7 F
8 W	8 S
9 T	9 S
10 F	10 M
11 S	11 T
12 S	12 W
13 M	13 T
14 T	14 F
15 W	15 S
16 T	16 S
17 F	17 M
18 S	18 T
19 S	19 W
20 M	20 T
21 T	21 F
22 W	22 S
23 T	23 S
24 F	24 M
25 S	25 T
26 S	26 W
27 M	27 T
28 T	28 F
29 W	
30 T	
31 F	

PLANNER

	MAY			JUNE
1	M		1	T
2	T		2	F
3	W		3	S
4	T		4	S
5	F		5	M
6	S		6	T
7	S		7	W
8	M		8	T
9	T		9	F
10	W		10	S
11	T		11	S
12	F		12	M
13	S		13	T
14	S		14	W
15	M		15	T
16	T		16	F
17	W		17	S
18	T		18	S
19	F		19	M
20	S		20	T
21	S		21	W
22	M		22	T
23	T		23	F
24	W		24	S
25	T		25	S
26	F		26	M
27	S		27	T
28	S		28	W
29	M		29	T
30	T		30	F
31	W			

JULY		AUGUST	
1 S		1 T	
2 S		2 W	
3 M		3 T	
4 T		4 F	
5 W		5 S	
6 T		6 S	
7 F		7 M	
8 S		8 T	
9 S		9 W	
10 M		10 T	
11 T		11 F	
12 W		12 S	
13 T		13 S	
14 F		14 M	
15 S		15 T	
16 S		16 W	
17 M		17 T	
18 T		18 F	
19 W		19 S	
20 T		20 S	
21 F		21 M	
22 S		22 T	
23 S		23 W	
24 M		24 T	
25 T		25 F	
26 W		26 S	
27 T		27 S	
28 F		28 M	
29 S		29 T	
30 S		30 W	
31 M		31 T	

PLANNER

SEPTEMBER	OCTOBER
1 F	
2 S	2 M
3 S	3 T
4 M	4 W
5 T	5 T
6 W	6 F
7 T	7 S
8 F	8 S
9 S	9 M
10 S	10 T
11 M	11 W
12 T	12 T
13 W	13 F
14 T	14 S
15 F	15 S
16 S	16 M
17 S	17 T
18 M	18 W
19 T	19 T
20 W	20 F
21 T	21 S
22 F	22 S
23 S	23 M
24 S	24 T
25 M	25 W
26 T	26 T
27 W	27 F
28 T	28 S
29 F	29 S
30 S	30 M
	31 T

NOVEMBER

1	W
2	T
3	F
4	S
5	S
6	M
7	T
8	W
9	T
10	F
11	S
12	S
13	M
14	T
15	W
16	T
17	F
18	S
19	S
20	M
21	T
22	W
23	T
24	F
25	S
26	S
27	M
28	T
29	W
30	T

DECEMBER

1	F
2	S
3	S
4	M
5	T
6	W
7	T
8	F
9	S
10	S
11	M
12	T
13	W
14	T
15	F
16	S
17	S
18	M
19	T
20	W
21	T
22	F
23	S
24	S
25	M
26	T
27	W
28	T
29	F

MON
26

TUE
27

WED
28

THU
29

FRI
30

SAT
31

NEW YEAR'S DAY

SUN
1

CLIFF

JANUARY

MON
2

NEW YEAR HOLIDAY

TUE
3

BANK HOLIDAY (SCOTLAND)

WED
4

THU
5

FRI
6

SAT
7

SUN
8

JANUARY

MON
9

TUE
10

WED
11

THU
12

FRI
13

SAT
14

SUN
15

JANUARY

MON
16

TUE
17

WED
18

THU
19

FRI
20

SAT
21

CHINESE NEW YEAR (RABBIT)

SUN
22

JANUARY

MON
23

....

TUE
24

....

WED
25

....

THU
26

....

FRI
27

....

SAT
28

....

SUN
29

JAN / FEB

MON
30

TUE
31

WED
1

THU
2

FRI
3

SAT
4

SUN
5

FEBRUARY

MON
6

....

TUE
7

....

WED
8

....

THU
9

....

FRI
10

....

SAT
11

....

SUN
12

FEBRUARY

MON
13

VALENTINE'S DAY

TUE
14

WED
15

THU
16

FRI
17

SAT
18

SUN
19

FEBRUARY

MON
20

TUE
21

SHROVE TUESDAY

WED
22

THU
23

FRI
24

SAT
25

SUN
26

FEB / MAR

MON
27

TUE
28

ST. DAVID'S DAY

WED
1

THU
2

FRI
3

SAT
4

SUN
5

MARCH

MON
6

TUE
7

WED
8

THU
9

FRI
10

SAT
11

SUN
12

CLIFF

MARCH

MON
13

....

TUE
14

....

WED
15

....

THU
16

....

ST. PATRICK'S DAY

FRI
17

....

SAT
18

....

MOTHERING SUNDAY (UK)

SUN
19

MARCH

MON
20

TUE
21

RAMADAN BEGINS

WED
22

THU
23

FRI
24

SAT
25

DAYLIGHT SAVING TIME STARTS

SUN
26

MAR / APR

MON
27

TUE
28

WED
29

THU
30

FRI
31

SAT
1

SUN
2

APRIL

MON
3

TUE
4

PASSOVER BEGINS

WED
5

THU
6

GOOD FRIDAY

FRI
7

SAT
8

EASTER SUNDAY

SUN
9

APRIL

MON
10

TUE
11

WED
12

THU
13

FRI
14

SAT
15

SUN
16

APRIL

MON
17

TUE
18

WED
19

THU
20

FRI
21

SAT
22

EARTH DAY

SUN
23

ST. GEORGE'S DAY

APRIL

MON
24

TUE
25

WED
26

THU
27

FRI
28

SAT
29

SUN
30

MAY

MON
1

TUE
2

WED
3

THU
4

FRI
5

SAT
6

SUN
7

Photograph by Zoë Gates

CLIFF

MAY

MON
8

TUE
9

WED
10

THU
11

FRI
12

SAT
13

SUN
14

MAY

MON
15

TUE
16

WED
17

THU
18

FRI
19

SAT
20

SUN
21

MAY

MON
22

....

TUE
23

....

WED
24

....

THU
25

....

FRI
26

....

SAT
27

....

SUN
28

MAY / JUN

SPRING BANK HOLIDAY

MON
29

TUE
30

WED
31

THU
1

FRI
2

SAT
3

SUN
4

JUNE

MON
5

TUE
6

WED
7

THU
8

FRI
9

SAT
10

SUN
11

JUNE

MON
12

....

TUE
13

....

WED
14

....

THU
15

....

FRI
16

....

SAT
17

....

FATHER'S DAY (UK)

SUN
18

JUNE

MON
19

TUE
20

WED
21

THU
22

FRI
23

SAT
24

SUN
25

JUN / JUL

MON
26

TUE
27

WED
28

THU
29

FRI
30

SAT
1

SUN
2

CLIFF

JULY

MON
3

TUE
4

WED
5

THU
6

FRI
7

SAT
8

SUN
9

JULY

MON
10

TUE
11

PUBLIC HOLIDAY (NORTHERN IRELAND)

WED
12

THU
13

FRI
14

SAT
15

SUN
16

JULY

MON
17

TUE
18
ISLAMIC NEW YEAR BEGINS

WED
19

THU
20

FRI
21

SAT
22

SUN
23

JULY

MON
24

TUE
25

WED
26

THU
27

FRI
28

SAT
29

SUN
30

JUL / AUG

MON
31

TUE
1

WED
2

THU
3

FRI
4

SAT
5

SUN
6

CLIFF

AUGUST

MON
7

....

TUE
8

....

WED
9

....

THU
10

....

FRI
11

....

SAT
12

....

SUN
13

AUGUST

MON
14

TUE
15

WED
16

THU
17

FRI
18

SAT
19

SUN
20

AUGUST

MON
21

TUE
22

WED
23

THU
24

FRI
25

SAT
26

SUN
27

AUG / SEPT

SUMMER BANK HOLIDAY (ENG, NIR, WAL)

MON
28

....

TUE
29

....

WED
30

....

THU
31

....

FRI
1

....

SAT
2

....

SUN
3

SEPTEMBER

MON
4

TUE
5

WED
6

THU
7

FRI
8

SAT
9

SUN
10

CLIFF

SEPTEMBER

MON
11

TUE
12

WED
13

THU
14

ROSH HASHANAH (JEWISH NEW YEAR) BEGINS

FRI
15

SAT
16

SUN
17

SEPTEMBER

MON
18

TUE
19

WED
20

INTERNATIONAL DAY OF PEACE (UNITED NATIONS)

THU
21

FRI
22

SAT
23

YOM KIPPUR BEGINS

SUN
24

SEPT / OCT

MON
25

TUE
26

WED
27

THU
28

FRI
29

SAT
30

SUN
1

CLIFF

OCTOBER

MON
2

TUE
3

WED
4

THU
5

FRI
6

SAT
7

SUN
8

OCTOBER

MON
9

TUE
10

WORLD MENTAL HEALTH DAY

WED
11

THU
12

FRI
13

SAT
14

SUN
15

OCTOBER

MON
16

TUE
17

WED
18

THU
19

FRI
20

SAT
21

SUN
22

OCTOBER

MON
23

TUE
24

WED
25

THU
26

FRI
27

SAT
28

DAYLIGHT SAVING TIME ENDS

SUN
29

OCT / NOV

MON
30

TUE
31

HALLOWEEN

WED
1

THU
2

FRI
3

SAT
4

SUN
5

GUY FAWKES NIGHT

CLIFF

NOVEMBER

MON
6

TUE
7

WED
8

THU
9

FRI
10

SAT
11

DIWALI & REMEMBRANCE SUNDAY
SUN
12

NOVEMBER

MON
13

TUE
14

WED
15

THU
16

FRI
17

SAT
18

SUN
19

NOVEMBER

MON
20

TUE
21

WED
22

THU
23

FRI
24

SAT
25

SUN
26

NOV / DEC

MON
27

TUE
28

WED
29

ST. ANDREW'S DAY

THU
30

FRI
1

SAT
2

SUN
3

DECEMBER

MON
4

TUE
5

WED
6

THU
7

FRI
8

SAT
9

SUN
10

DECEMBER

MON
11

TUE
12

WED
13

THU
14

FRI
15

SAT
16

SUN
17

DECEMBER

MON
18

TUE
19

WED
20

THU
21

FRI
22

SAT
23

SUN
24

DECEMBER

MON
25
CHRISTMAS DAY

TUE
26
BOXING DAY

WED
27

THU
28

FRI
29

SAT
30

SUN
31
NEW YEAR'S EVE

JANUARY 24

MON
1

TUE
2

WED
3

THU
4

FRI
5

SAT
6

SUN
7

CONTACTS

....

NAME:
....

....

ADDRESS:
....

....

....

....

....

PHONE:
....

E-MAIL:
....

....

NAME:
....

....

ADDRESS:
....

....

....

....

....

PHONE:
....

E-MAIL:
....

CONTACTS

NAME:

ADDRESS:

PHONE:

E-MAIL:

NAME:

ADDRESS:

PHONE:

E-MAIL:

CONTACTS

....

NAME:

....

ADDRESS:

....

....

....

....

PHONE:

E-MAIL:

....

NAME:

....

ADDRESS:

....

....

....

....

PHONE:

E-MAIL:

CONTACTS

NAME:

ADDRESS:

PHONE:

E-MAIL:

NAME:

ADDRESS:

PHONE:

E-MAIL:

CONTACTS

NAME: ....
....

ADDRESS: ....
....
....
....
....

PHONE: ....

E-MAIL: ....

NAME: ....
....

ADDRESS: ....
....
....
....

PHONE: ....

E-MAIL: ....

CONTACTS

NAME:

ADDRESS:

PHONE:

E-MAIL:

NAME:

ADDRESS:

PHONE:

E-MAIL:

CONTACTS

NAME:

ADDRESS:

PHONE:

E-MAIL:

NAME:

ADDRESS:

PHONE:

E-MAIL:

CONTACTS

NAME:

ADDRESS:

PHONE:

E-MAIL:

NAME:

ADDRESS:

PHONE:

E-MAIL:

NOTES

NOTES